MODERN PARTRIDGE FARMING

BY
CHRIS HODGSON

Edited by
Michael D L Roberts & Sara Roadnight
with assistance from Tim & Daniel Farr

Section on diseases by Alan Beynon
of St David's Game Bird Services
Exmouth, Devon

The Author

Chris Hodgson was born in North Devon, and started rearing
pheasants on a small farm. He has gradually built up a commercial
partridge and pheasant rearing concern supplying estates and farms
throughout the UK and Ireland. He has been rearing English and French
partridges commercially for more than 15 years.

© 2009 Michael Roberts
published by Gold Cockerel Books
ISBN 978 0947870 621

CONTENTS

Chapter	Page
The English Partridge	1
The Red-legged Partridge	4
Plumage differences and Sexing	6
The Various Markets for Reared Partridges	10
Before you Start	11
Rearing Houses	13
Shelters	15
Construction of Shelters and Sections	16
The Rearing Field	22
Setting up the Rearing Field	23
Rearing with Gas	27
Rearing with Electricity	29
On the Rearing Field	32
Day 1 to Week 4	35
Week 4	36
Week 5 to 8	37
Week 9 to 14	39
Catching and Transport	41
The Release Pen	47
Releasing the Birds	50
Tagging	53
Laying Pens and Feeding	55
Preparation of Eggs	63
Bought in Eggs	64
Your own Eggs	64
Incubation	65
Out of the Hatcher	66
When the Birds have Gone	71
Conservation of English Partridge	73
Predators	77
Partridge Diseases	80
Useful Contacts	90
Index	91

The English Partridge
Perdix perdix, sometimes Perdix cinerea.

The English partridge is sometimes called the Common or Grey partridge. It is non migratory.

These birds are found mainly on farmed land, especially on light soils and arable land where they frequent the rough ground bordering cultivation. In coastal areas they like to feed on the shoreline. They avoid heavy clay soils, which crack in hot summers and would cause the loss of many chicks down the crevices. English partridges are not as widespread as 50 years ago, due to intensive cultivation, hedge removal and above all the use of chemical sprays which is an on-going problem. They are found on large estates and keepered farms (where people are aware of the partridges' needs) in the South of England, East Anglia, parts of the Midlands, and scattered areas across the rest of the British Isles.

Partridges are a prey species and their presence shows a good equilibrium between prey and predator, a healthy sign of balance in the countryside.

They are easily recognisable, being smallish round birds, weighing about 350gms, with orange-brown heads, greyish under parts, chestnut barred flanks and grey legs. The two sexes look alike from a distance, but in fact the crown on the cock bird is brown, with the rest of the head and neck red; the hen bird just has a brown head. The cock bird also has a bold brown horseshoe on his chest which can be seen on hen birds as well although to a lesser extent. The horseshoe markings vary according to the age of bird and the season. Cock birds have no spurs and are more upright in appearance than females.

English partridges have the largest vocabulary of all game birds, as they cluck, chatter, hiss, bill snap and use a guttural note of alarm "br-r-r-r". The most common call is a loud, hoarse, "karwit, karwit" or "kirr-ie, kirr-ie".

They are found in coveys, small groups or pairs, but rarely singly except during the breeding season. They pair up before French partridges, and this can be any time from the end of November through to February. They are great fighters over territory, and can be seen in spring time running to and fro, engaged in furious battles, quite oblivious to passing danger. They will nest in fields of corn or grass and on roadsides, but prefer sunny banks out of the prevailing wind that catch the early morning sun; in the old days when fields were much smaller than to-day, it was fairly easy for an experienced eye to spot a nest. There is normally a run through the grass, similar to a rabbit run but not so marked, and this will lead to a shallow scrape in the ground and an exit run. The hen bird does like some light cover overhead. The eggs are olive/khaki/brown in colour, normally about 10 to 14; this will vary if a hen bird has lost a nest and is laying for the second time when it could be as few as 8 eggs. There are records of more than 16 eggs in a nest, but this is due to a second hen laying in the same place.

The cock bird plays little part in the incubation of the eggs which takes 23 to 24 days. Once the chicks hatch both birds are very attentive: the hen will do the broken wing act to draw away a person, a dog or a fox from the brood. The young will flutter at 10-11 days, fly a little at 16 days and at 3 weeks will fly quite well. Later, when they are disturbed, they will burst into the air, shouting, and with a series of quick wing beats followed by a glide, will be away. They do tend to know where they are going and how to keep safe, much to the chagrin of the hunter. At some times of year, particularly late summer, it is almost possible to step on a covey accidentally as they will sit so tight that they are nearly invisible. They are ground birds, preferring to walk or run rather than fly to cover. They love to dust bath.

Food is varied depending on the season. It can be as high as 60% vegetable matter – weed seeds, cereals, buckwheat, clover, grasses, sugar beet, brassicas etc, and 40% animal foods which include earthworms, slugs, beetles, ants, spiders, snails, etc.

English partridges do not perch, although there have been rare sightings of this. At night time they roost or 'jug' close together on open ground well away from hedges and cover, lying in a rough circle or arc, heads turned outwards. If disturbed, they will scatter in all directions, thus foiling the intruder as well as avoiding collision among themselves. Evidence of this is quite easy to see when the ground is frosty. They were frequently poached at night because they sat so tight.

Mutations in colour are rare but do occur in English partridges. Albino birds are seen from time to time, and a covey of black partridges was spotted in Warwickshire near the village of Barton in 1970.

The Red-legged Partridge.
Alectoris rufa.

The red-legged partridge is commonly called the French partridge and is referred to as that throughout this book. It is a non migratory bird.

The French partridge is actually related more closely to a francolin, the male having spur nodules. It is not a native breed but was originally introduced into England about 1673 during the reign of Charles II. It was released in Windsor and Richmond Parks, but this was not successful. In 1770 it was reintroduced, this time at Orford, Suffolk and again in 1823 at Calford, Bury St Edmunds, when a quantity of eggs was imported from France. The French partridge then started to breed naturally much to the chagrin of local people who despised all things French, because of the Napoleanic Wars.

The French partridge is larger than the English partridge, 500gms (male) 450gms (female), and looks quite different, with white cheeks and throat bordered by a black band. The flanks are barred with black, white and chestnut, and it has a red bill and legs. The back is a drab brown which gives the bird excellent camouflage when it is squatting tight on the ground. The first flight feather is not shed at the first autumnal moult. Instead of being rounded, it is pointed like a lance and there is a yellowish-white patch near the tip; this serves to differentiate a young bird from an old bird.

The two sexes look alike, but the male is larger by about 50gms, having slightly more pronounced black throat markings, and of course spur nodules. These are not spurs as you see in pheasants, more blunt bumps on the leg where the spur would be. French partridges are more striking than the smaller drab English partridge which again, didn't endear them to the East Anglians at the time of introduction.

These partridges are more nervous than the English partridge. In the rearing pen they appear to be constantly on the go, and in the wild, they run even more than the English, preferring it to flying. When they do get off the ground, rarely as a covey, more in ones and twos, they are strong fliers. They perch fairly frequently on gates, fences, walls and even barns. There are some estates and large farms who still will not countenance French partridges even to-day, just sticking to rearing English partridges.

The French partridge is at home on any heavy or light farm land, although its feet and toes nails can become balled up with mud. It does prefer drier areas, as it is a bird of rocky and arid country.

These birds make an unmistakeable harsh call, " chuka-chuka" or "chik-chik-chikar", and sometimes "shack-shack-shack-shack-shack", which carries a fair distance on a still frosty day. They will nest anywhere where it is quiet, hedgerows, fields, young plantations or waste areas. The nest is a simple scrape in the ground usually sheltered by long grass or bushes. They lay about 10 to16 eggs, sometimes fewer, 7 to 8, if it is a second nest. The egg colour varies from an ashy cream to buffy brown, sometimes lightly or heavily speckled with brown spots or splashes.

Some people wonder how partridges are able to lay 60 eggs or more in pens. The answer is in the feeding: they have a high protein breeding pellet, and naturally they have no predator worries. Of course they are not encouraged to go broody, as the eggs are collected daily.

Incubation time is 23 days. The cock bird is known to help out with incubation. French partridges seem to be more prolific than English partridges; they are bigger birds and maybe they lay slightly larger clutches. The food of the French partridge is mostly vegetable matter, cereals, weed seeds, grasses, clovers, peas, beans, acorns and beech mast to name a few of the things in their diet. They eat far fewer insects than the English partridge which has been badly affected by chemical sprays.

Plumage Differences and Sexing

English partridge (young birds)
The leg colour can be yellowy grey, the two outer primary feathers are pointed and the third primary is shorter in the summer and autumn.
English partridge (adult)
The leg colour is grey and the outer primary feathers are rounded. The cock bird has no spurs. The female has blackish transverse bars on the median tertiary wing feathers, while the same feathers on the cock bird are mottled grey or brown. All males have a dark brown horse shoe mark on the breast which is also carried in various shades and patterns by hen birds. The male has a brown cap on top of the head during the winter and breeding season. He also shows a red wattle line in varying amounts around the eye.
There is little difference in size and weight, between the two sexes.

Male   Female

French partridge (young birds)
Both have a buff tip to the first flight feather on the wing.
French partridge (adult)
The male is larger than the female by about 100gms in weight.
Both males and females carry a spur nodule on the leg but the male's is more pronounced.
Both male and female can be vent sexed.

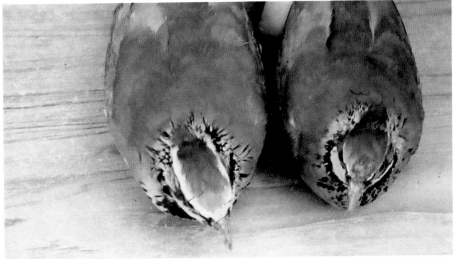

Male   *Female*

Vent sexing adult French partridges, the male above and female below

The Various Markets for Reared Partridges

1) Hatching eggs.
2) Day old chicks.
3) Poults from 8 to 18 weeks old.
4) Adult young birds for breeding.
5) Adult layers at the end of laying.

1) Hatching eggs. These are supplied washed and ready to go into the incubator on egg trays. They should arrive with the customer 48 hours before they are set, to allow them to settle after the journey in a cool room (temperature 10 - 12 °C). They should be no more than 7days old. Most partridge eggs today are supplied from France.

2) Day old chicks. These are incubator hatched and delivered within 24 hours. They are normally sent in special chick boxes with four compartments, 38 chicks in 3 compartments and 39 in the forth, a total of 153 chicks: the Game Farmers' Association dictate a 2% oversupply. These boxes travel in a temperature controlled van, set at 26 degrees C to ensure that the chicks arrive in good condition.

3) Poults from 8 to 18 weeks old. Both English and French partridges are caught up and crated, (35 to 40 per crate) and sold to the customer for further rearing or releasing. Some people now require a vet's certificate on arrival.

4) Adult young birds for breeding. These birds can be anywhere between 18 to 24 weeks old. They are caught up, sexed, and put in separate crates by sex, normally 35 to the crate, prior to delivery and being placed in breeding pens.

5) Adult layers at the end of laying. These are birds which have been in the laying pens, and are due for release after they have moulted, normally in August.

Before You Start

Before you start there are a number of things you need to be aware of. You may have reared chickens, turkeys or pheasants, but partridges are a big step up from these birds, particularly if the season is wet when there could be problems. The rearing set up is similar to that of pheasants but there the similarity ends. Partridges come from drier climes and the French partridge from very arid and often rocky areas. In dry summers there is normally no problem, but if the season is wet you will have to work very closely with your local specialist avian vet. Partridges are more susceptible to diseases than pheasants.

If you have not already got some, you will need a flock of sheep to mow the grass in the pens before the birds are released into them. Once the birds have reached 8 weeks of age, when they have been out on the grass for 3 weeks, a sample of 2 birds per batch must be post-mortemed weekly to check that they are healthy, as very often they do not show any symptoms of ill health. The last thing you want is to deliver diseased birds, or birds that are going to die, or birds so full of drugs that they are rendered inedible; close cooperation with your specialist vet and food supplier is vital, as not all drugs are water borne. So you are sacrificing birds from each batch on a weekly basis until they are delivered to the customer. Some customers now require a vet's bill of clean health upon delivery.

One good point is that the release pen will normally be on fresh ground and the birds will certainly thrive, but it is imperative that they leave your place in tip-top condition.

Some vets require a 'clean' room set aside on your premises with a minimum of hot and cold water and electricity, in order to post-mortem your birds as

Sheep are used to graze the pens before the young birds are released into the grass pens. There may be a time lapse of 4 - 8 weeks between the pen going up and the birds being released. Timing is important, as the sheep must be withdrawn soon enough to avoid a problem with faecal contamination but the grass must not be too long for the young birds.

freshly as possible.

It's important to begin slowly and carefully; many people have burned their fingers by going too fast. It is a specialised market, and you will have to gain the confidence of the buyers, particularly in wet years. There are several companies that have been rearing partridges for a long time, and edging in on their market could prove difficult. If you have reared pheasants then you are half way there, as the housing and pens are similar.

Rearing Houses

There are three types of rearing house, which are also suitable for pheasants. For partridges they require an extra door opposite the entrance into the shelter; this is for people to use at catching time.

The first type of house is a simple 8ft by 8ft square complete with floor which sits on the ground. As with all the houses, it must be level so that the floor drinkers don't spill over, and you can achieve this by using different sized pieces of wood to shore it up where necessary. Some people don't like these houses because you have to crawl in to service them, although knee pads help: the maximum height of the roof is only 4ft. The floor (which is not attached to the walls) is made of half or three quarter inch thick plywood on a frame of 2" x 1" or 2" x 2" tanalised timber. The door is either in the middle between two ventilation windows or at one end with a single ventilation window. Most of these houses have plyboard roofs covered with black plastic sheeting.

The second type of house covers approximately the same floor area, but has an apex roof and is taller, being 6ft at the apex, so some people will be able to stand up inside it. There is a central door and two ventilation windows. It costs a little more to heat but is easier to service. Both these houses have room for 450 birds, one gas brooder, two food hoppers, two floor drinkers and two nipple drinkers; it is important that the birds learn to use both types of drinker.

The third type of house is larger at 12ft by 12ft and is still at an experimental stage. Because it is so big it needs two gas brooders, four nipple drinkers and four food hoppers, and the outside area must be double the normal size. When dealing with this number of birds under one roof it is essential that the management is spot on.

8ft × 8ft rearing house

8ft × 8ft apex rearing house. Note the outside pop holes on both houses for catching up young adult birds

14

Shelters

These come in two designs, 'A' frame and square. The 'A' frame type has a floor area of 8ft by 4ft and is approximately 5ft high. It consists of two 'A' frame ends, two sides and a floor.

The square type is approximately 8ft by 8ft and is the same size as the rearing house but without a floor.

Construction of Shelters
and Sections

Materials used:

Treated 2☐ x 1☐ or 5 x 2.5cm

Treated 6☐ x 1☐ or 15 x 2.5cm

1☐ wire netting or mesh x 4ft wide (50 metre rolls)

8ft x 4ft x ☐☐ (12mm) ply board (treated if possible)

Monarflex, woven plastic sheeting in rolls 50m x 1.1m wide.

The 10ft x 5ft sections are best made on jigs. This way they can be quickly made once the material is cut to size.

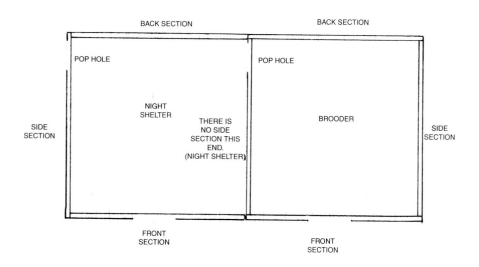

BACK SECTION   BACK SECTION

POP HOLE   POP HOLE

NIGHT SHELTER

THERE IS NO SIDE SECTION THIS END. (NIGHT SHELTER)

BROODER

SIDE SECTION   SIDE SECTION

FRONT SECTION   FRONT SECTION

Shelter Side Section
Facing the Run

INSIDE

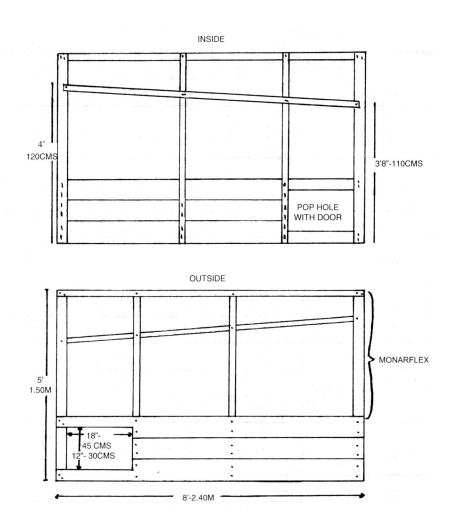

4'
120CMS

3'8"-110CMS

POP HOLE
WITH DOOR

OUTSIDE

MONARFLEX

5'
1.50M

18"-
45 CMS
12"- 30CMS

8'-2.40M

Shelter Pen

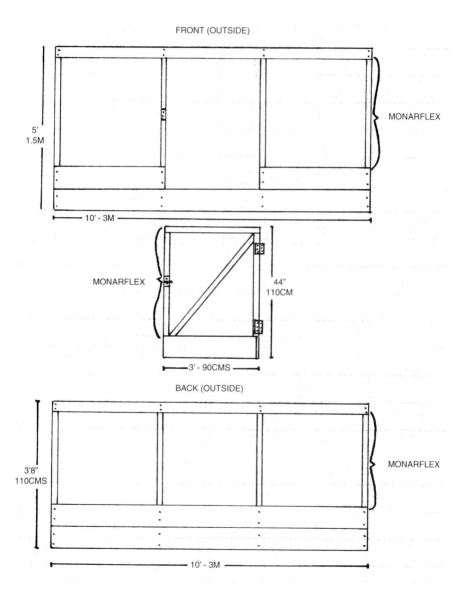

FRONT (OUTSIDE)

MONARFLEX

5'
1.5M

10' - 3M

MONARFLEX

44"
110CM

3' - 90CMS

BACK (OUTSIDE)

3'8"
110CMS

MONARFLEX

10' - 3M

18

Shelter Roof

ROOF COVERED WITH MONARFLEX

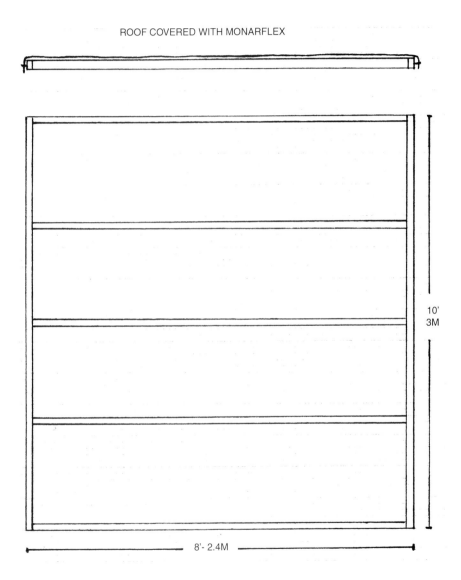

10'
3M

8'- 2.4M

19

Sections
Gate Section

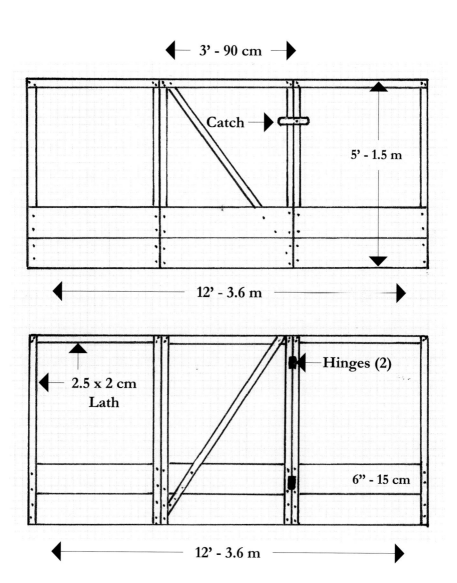

3' - 90 cm

Catch →

5' - 1.5 m

12' - 3.6 m

2.5 x 2 cm
Lath

Hinges (2)

6" - 15 cm

12' - 3.6 m

Standard 10ft sections

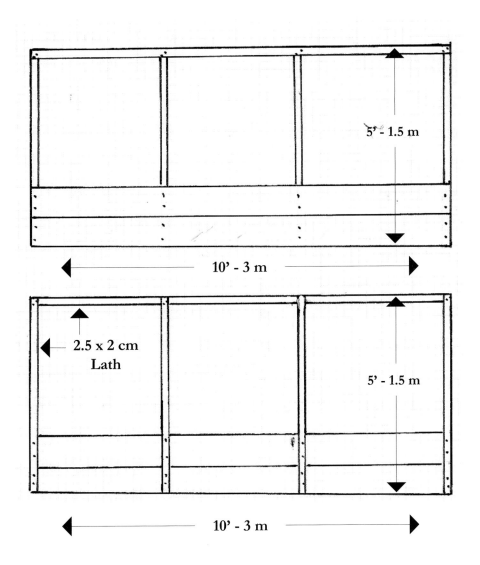

5' - 1.5 m

10' - 3 m

2.5 x 2 cm
Lath

5' - 1.5 m

10' - 3 m

The Rearing Field.

The rearing field needs several pre-requisites before you choose and use it.
1) The field needs to be quiet and away from roads and footpaths.
2) It should be south facing to receive the maximum sunshine.
3) It needs to be large enough for the pens and houses, with access between them.
4) It requires mains water or some other reliable water source.
5) It has to be gently sloping, for the gravity fed drinkers.
6) It must have a good clean mixture of grass and clover.
7) It needs good access with metalled roadways.

A good metalled road is vital for access to the rearing field, as there will always be more traffic to and from the site than you think: tractors and trailers bringing in equipment and taking it out at the end of the season, food being brought in continually, young birds being taken out, not to mention the daily traffic of four by fours and quad bikes; so obviously good access is essential, particularly in a year like 2008 when it seemed to rain most of the summer. The last thing you want is a feed lorry getting stuck or deep ruts caused by tractors.

Setting up the Rearing Field.

Depending on the number of pens required this could begin in March; remember, the first chicks should be hatched by the end of April.
There should be 5 to 7 yards between one line of houses and the next, giving you plenty of room for access. The outside pens should measure 30ft by 50ft.

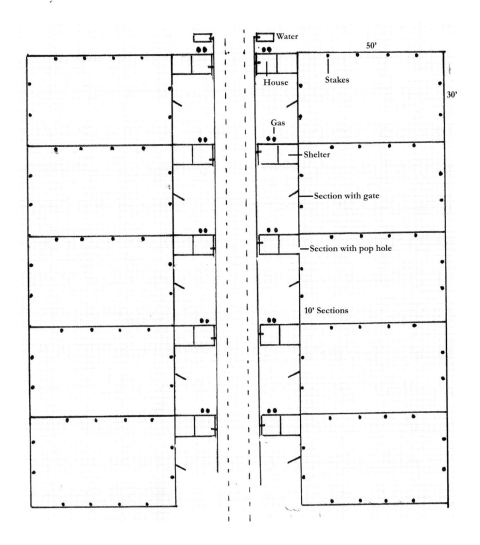

All the heavy components need to be brought in first: the 10ft sections and 6ft stakes, the house parts, and the shelter parts.

You will need plastic ties, (for fixing the stakes to the sections and the sections to each other), green netting, roof netting and blocks of wood for levelling the house and shelter.

First start by laying a nice straight line of sections on the ground down the slope, leaving about 20 yards between them and the hedge. The sections are held upright and attached with plastic ties to 6ft stakes thumped into the ground where they meet, but not at the corners. Next, attach the green netting all the way round the inside of the pen by hanging it from nails that you have knocked into the top rail of each section. Then start to add the five 10ft cross sections at right angles where the third and fourth sections meet, and at each third section along. Do not erect the two middle ones but leave the stakes ready to attach them to. There are two reasons for this: first, the men can move much more easily from pen to pen as they work, particularly when putting up the overhead netting; secondly, it allows room for your sheep to come in and graze the grass nice and short during the 2 to 3 months before the birds are put in. The centre sections are tied against the fixed sections while the sheep are there. Grass must be kept short for partridges because if it is allowed to become long and lank it gets flattened and the birds' droppings would rest on top and become a health hazard; if the grass is short, then the droppings are better absorbed into the ground. Mowing such an area is impractical, because the clippings have to be removed as they too can set up fungus and bacterial health problems.

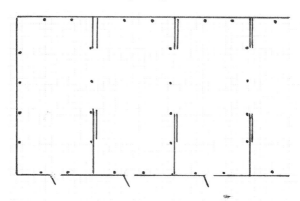

Pens ready for sheep grazing

Once the cross sections have been dealt with, then the side of the pen that contains the birds' access to the shelter and house can be set up. This involves a 'normal' section, a gate section (for people) and a pophole section. When these are in place the roof netting can be installed. This comes in a long coil, tied every three feet to hold it together, and is rolled onto the roof and the ties cut. Then it is stretched out and clipped to the wire netting on the outside sections with plastic 'S' clips. You must also be aware that partridges will need some shade from the sun on very hot days. The pens do not provide any shelter but this can be achieved with some Netlon: unroll a 5m roll of this green netting over the top of the roof netting and fix it at both ends. It can either be taken away when the weather gets cooler or kept in place, rolled up at one end of the roof, ready to be used again when necessary.

Next the shelters are assembled and positioned up against the popholes; the houses are then attached to the shelters. Some people like to bolt these together, others use small coach screws and a battery powered hand gun which makes the job faster. The house must then be levelled with blocks of wood because of the chick floor drinkers.

An A frame shelter, gas bottle and apex house

25

The next item is the header tank, which stands at the top end of the field, by the first house; there is one for each row of houses. It is normally raised on pallets to about 5 or 6ft high. Plastic piping is uncoiled down the field beside the row of houses, with a connecting tube to each house. The tube is bent double to prevent water from flowing and remains like this until connected to a drinker or nipple drinker. Several 'T' connectors may be used.

The water source (mains or otherwise) is connected to the header tank which is filled up and turned on to check that all connections are watertight. Having a leak in a house can lead to all sorts of problems, soggy litter, wet food, aspergillosis, etc. so this must be checked thoroughly.

Next, put in the gas bottles.

Water header tank and pipes

Rearing with Gas

Gas can be organised in two ways: you can have two bottles and a change-over valve next to each house but out of the main carriage way, or a cluster of bottles with change-over valves at the top of each row. If you use the latter, then you will require a long lead pipe beside the water pipe with a 'T' gas pipe junction at each house. When these are in place, it is advisable to spray the grass along the pipes, so they can be seen and are not cut up with the mower or strimmer.

The gas heaters need to be hung 70cms above the litter in the houses to create a hot spot of 100 to 105 degrees on the litter below; this ensures that the chicks will move away from the intense heat and find the food and water.

The gas used is normal propane gas which comes in large metal cylinders (47kg). In an average year you will require three and a half bottles for each house containing 450 chicks, but this can obviously vary depending on the weather. There are several types of gas heater on the market. They are normally very reliable, and most modern ones have a flame failure device which shuts off the gas if the flame goes out. However, the flames in some older heaters can sometimes be blown out by chicks fluttering round if they have been spooked, and they often blow out the gas when they start to fly at about 4 weeks old; they love to cruise round trying out their wings, particularly in the early mornings between 1 and 2am and again at 4 and 5am. This is why it is so important to make regular checks, every 2 hours for the first 2 days and every 3 hours after that. If the flames are blown out the gas continues to escape and sinks to the floor, gassing the chicks. Because of this it's vital to carry a gas detector whenever you enter a house: you won't be able to smell gas as it is down at floor level. It is even more important that you never smoke while doing your rounds and feeding the birds, as there have been some dreadful accidents and burns resulting from this. If you do find that the flames have gone out when you enter a house, the first thing to do is turn off the gas then open the door and ventilation windows and fan the gas outside. If you have managed to save the birds, you must check with the detector before lighting the heater again.

An 8ft × 8ft rearing house with plastic sheet roof covering.
Note the house is raised up in the front to ensure the floor is level.

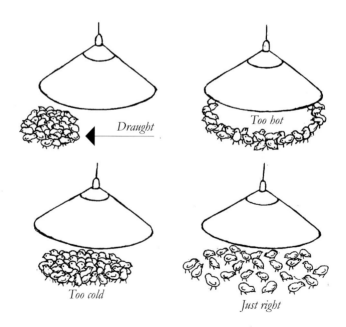

These diagrams show how chicks disperse or crowd together if there is a draught in the
rearing area, or if they are too hot or too cold under the heat lamp. It also shows their
distribution under the lamp when all conditions are ideal.

Rearing with Electricity

Not many people use this method as it requires a good reliable supply of electricity to a rural shed or barn in a field. It also means that you are restricted to using the same ground all the time or using alternate sides of the building to rear your partridges on.

This system uses low wattage 'electric hens' to keep the chicks warm; electric hens are rectangular heated pads which are supported on adjustable legs and the chicks creep under them for warmth. An electric hen measuring 48" x 30" has room for 250 partridge chicks. This system actually produces the best chicks that have very few vices such as vent, toe or wing pecking, but it is vital to maintain an even temperature in the building if you are going to be successful. For the first week at least the temperature of the room should be 80 degrees or preferably 90 degrees F. It is useful to hang a thermometer just above the birds as a temperature check.

The floor in the building should be smooth concrete and the pens need to be 10 or 12ft square. Inside each pen you will need to construct 2 round enclosures which are made of 2ft wide hardboard clipped together to make a circle about 5ft in diameter. Put down some corrugated paper first then some chopped cardboard on top inside each enclosure; shavings are not used at this stage as very young chicks will try to eat them. Next put in an electric hen, 2 or 3 red floor feed pans and 2 quill drinkers. The chicks are introduced and tucked under the electric hens; they will come out to feed, drink and explore but the hardboard surround stops them wandering away too far and getting cold. The lighting is subdued. After 10 days the hardboard surrounds are removed and the chicks have full use of the pen which is covered with shavings instead of chopped cardboard. They are reared in this controlled environment for 6 weeks and start to sleep away from the heat during the fourth and fifth weeks; at this stage the electric hens can be safely removed.

One drawback to this system is that you can't see under the electric hens so you have to lift them every time you check the pen in order to see if there are any dead birds underneath. This method is far cheaper than heating by gas as long as the building is well insulated and ventilated.

At week 6 the pop holes to the outside pen are opened. You will have to cut the grass short and clear up the clippings before the birds come out, and

Note the electric hen and two quill drinkers, and the cardboard surround behind.

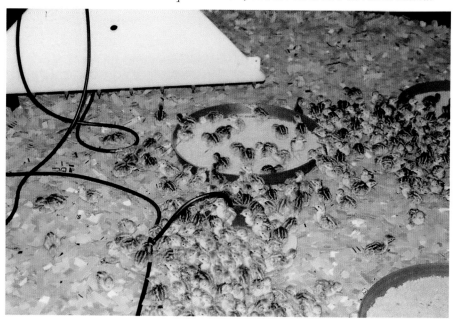

Note the banked-up corners, and two types of drinker: quill and floor type.

30

you may need to gently encourage them as they will be rather reluctant at first; keep a look out for rain, as they will need chivvying in out of the wet as well. They will soon get the hang of it and eventually will stay out all the time.

The birds will need 2 bell drinkers and 2 covered food hoppers in the run. At week 14 they are ready to be caught up in the shed and taken to the release pen.

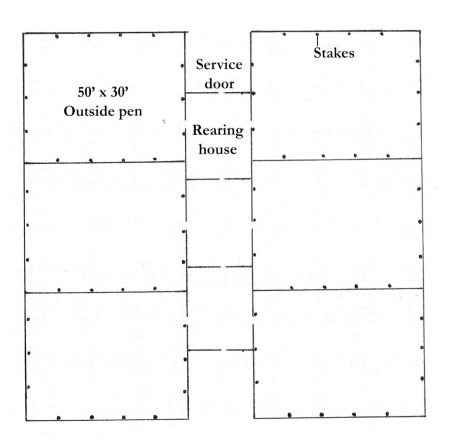

Diagram of one method of rearing with electric hens, with the shed in the middle and the outside pens either side.

On the Rearing Field

Before the chicks arrive:
You should decide how many pens you are going to use well before the chicks hatch so you have time to prepare the houses. Cover the floor first with corrugated paper then put down chipped cardboard all round the edges and bank it up in the corners to prevent chicks huddling together there and getting cold. If straw is used as litter and becomes damp there is a risk of mould developing which can cause Aspergillosis.

Daily records of mortalities and drug applications in each house.

Check that the water supply is working for both the floor drinkers and the nipple drinkers; adjust these to the correct height of 2 inches above the litter and place the floor pans on the floor. Twenty four hours before the hatch is due, turn on the gas heater, set it at 85 to 90 degrees, and make sure that it is running correctly so that the house will be warm for the chicks when they arrive. It is very important that the water in the drinkers is also warm before the chicks are put in; if they have travelled for some time before delivery (legally not more than 24 hours) they will be quite dehydrated and will drink almost immediately. If the water is cold they will damage their insides irreparably. Check the heater several times during the day to see if all is well.

Newly hatched chicks arrive and are put into their rearing houses.
Note the chipped cardboard on the floor.

Day One to Week Four.

The houses should all be fully prepared to receive the day old chicks. Before the chicks arrive, put out food in 3 feed pans and double check the water systems and gas. There should be 2 nipple drinkers and 2 floor drinkers available in each house. The ventilators should be open about 3 to 4" but this will depend on the weather at the time.

Put the chick boxes in the house and empty the chicks out gently. At this stage they are fairly quiet with only the odd rebellious one wanting to explore. Shut the door to conserve the heat, and have a look at them every 2 hours or as often as possible for the next 48 hours; that means someone will have to stay up to check on them through the night.

These chicks are past the 'starve out' stage and are begining to thrive.
The floor drinker is rasied on a stand and the food pans are replaced with food hoppers.

34

You can often tell, even before you open the door, if everything is all right inside: a cheeping noise means the gas has gone out and the chicks are cold which can lead to losses, if everything is silent it means that they are too hot and there is a danger of overcrowding, or it may mean that there is not enough ventilation, or worse still, they have been gassed. It's a good idea to whistle or tap on the door before you go in so that you don't alarm them. Don't forget, NEVER smoke when you go into the houses, and always carry a gas detector. The houses should smell dry and slightly acid inside, not at all damp; an unpleasant whiff means a dead body.

After the first 48 hours the chicks can be checked every 3 hours until they go out at 8 weeks.

For the first 2 weeks you will need guards or grids in the floor drinkers to prevent the chicks drowning. This type of drinker is notorious for leaking and will have to be cleaned each day. After about 2 weeks you can put these floor drinkers up onto plastic stands so that they don't fill up with debris as the chicks become more active.

The first week is when most of the birds that are not going to make it will die. This is natural: some cannot eat or drink, some do not develop properly, living the first day or so on the yolk that they absorbed from the egg and then giving up – these are called "starve-outs" as they are thin and their legs and feet are withered. A mortality card is pinned to the door of each house and a record of deaths is kept every morning and evening.

Feeding chicks

Start the chicks off with special partridge chick crumbs (protein 27 to 29%) in the red plastic floor pans; the chicks walk over them and peck at the food. After day 3 replace first one food pan with a food hopper then 3 days later replace the other food pans with a hopper. A lot of food is wasted from the pans so they should be removed as soon as possible. They can be washed and used for subsequent batches.

Week 4

English partridges must be bitted. These plastic clips are put in at week 4 and taken out at week 14 before the birds are released into the wild. Although they are quieter than their French counterparts, English partridges are more aggresive, and losses from fights and cannibalism can be very high if this is not done. The bit is slotted between the top and bottom parts of the beak and clipped into the nostrils with a hand held applicator. The bird can still eat, drink and breathe properly but is disarmed because it can't close its beak completely.

A hand held bitting gun.

Food: At this stage the young partridge can be moved onto rearer pellets (protein 22% - 24%)

Weeks 5 to 8

The young birds can now be allowed through to the shelter where there is a feed hopper and quill drinker or red bell drinker installed. The birds can still go back into the house but tend to spend more time in the shelter. The gas heater is turned off after seven and a half weeks and the cylinders can be removed.

Some young adult French partridges.

Week 8

If weather conditions are suitable the birds are now given access to the grass pen. Before this however, you will need to mow the grass round the inside edges of the pen and the area in front of the shelter; clear up the cut grass to prevent any fungus or bacteria growing on it as it dies. The short grass allows the birds to find their way round the pen and back to the shelter easily without getting too wet. You will need to install another bell drinker for them so put it in the area of short grass outside the shelter.

At week 8 the vet becomes involved, and a sample of 2 birds is taken from each batch to be post mortemed every week. This means that by the end of the 14th week, 12 birds from each batch will have been sacrificed in the interests of maintaining healthy stock. This is vital as partridges do not readily show any symptoms of disease, and often take 3 weeks to die. You can imagine the problems there would be if you delivered some birds which died after a week or two; no buyer would want to infect their stock of wild partridges. This is why most buyers require a veterinary clean bill of health to be delivered with their new stock. Many game farms have a special 'clean room' at their base with lights, tiled floors and hot and cold running water where the vets can check every bird for signs of disease.

Young adult French partridges. Note the outside feeder.

Weeks 9 to 14

At this stage the birds will start to fly round the pen, and this is where the green plastic netting comes in: it acts as a visual deterrent, preventing them from crashing into the sections and injuring or killing themselves, or even going right through the wire netting. If the birds were not running up and down and flying around it would be a sure sign that something was wrong. As they are spending more and more time outside, the feeders and drinkers can be put out with them, but don't forget to put weather-proof covers over the feeders.

Because French partridges spend so much time scuttling about, they create a problem with mud which in turn creates a potential foot problem for them. Muddy areas should be covered with straw which does two things: it prevents mud balling up on the birds' feet, and stops puddles forming where they would drink, a problem if you were treating them with a water based medicine. Balled up feet can be very difficult to deal with as the mud sets like concrete; the bird has difficulty moving about and can't drink or feed properly, sometimes losing a toe nail and causing bleeding. Birds with mud balled feet cannot be sold. This is one of the hazards of wet weather.

A good sign: French partridges flying around the pen.

A dry year

A wet year
In a wet year the outside run needs to be covered with
straw to prevent mud and puddles forming.

Catching and Transport.

This involves 4 people and the timing utterly depends on the weather forecast, as you can't catch in wet weather nor can you release in the rain. The Catcher is a tubular metal structure approximately 8ft by 10ft, clad in 1.5" Netlon, light enough to be carried by a couple of people. It is taken to the first house and set down up against the pop hole (see page 43). It contains two compartments, one where the birds are caught and the second where they are crated. There are two doors in the partition making an opening big enough for a person to get through.

A catching up pop hole.

Driving French partridges into the shelter.

A layer of straw is put down in the catching area if the ground is wet, and plastic crates are placed in the second compartment in a semi-circular fashion. The Catcher prevents any birds from escaping. The pop hole from the house into the Catcher is closed at this point. When the Catcher is in position, and everything is ready, two or three people enter the outside run and herd the birds towards the shelter. The door of the shelter must be open and the birds able to run through into the rearing house. When enough birds have gone through, the shelter door is closed and someone carefully gets into the shelter to push the remaining birds into the rearing house. Then he or she enters the rearing house to get the birds into the catcher. It is advisable to wear a face mask as this is dusty work.

When sufficient birds are inside (150 for example) the shelter door is closed; one person quietly enters the shelter via another door and pushes the birds through to the house. The pop hole into the house is closed and the pop hole into the Catcher is opened, and someone enters the house carefully to push the birds through to the Catcher. You must try to avoid having too many birds in the house or in the Catcher at any one time so they are not scrambling over each other. It's easy to lose a few birds at this stage by being careless, because if they pile up in the corners they will suffocate and die.

The door into the house is closed and two people enter the catching area from the crating area via the window. It is at this stage that English partridges have their bits removed: run your hand from the back of the head to the beak and the bit will slide out.

The Catcher showing the two compartments, one for catching, and the second for counting and crating the birds via a central window.

The partridges are caught five at a time and held by the legs in bunches; they are then passed through the window to the person crating the birds. Thirty five birds, that is 7 bunches, are placed in each crate via the release trap door. At the end there are always a few birds left in the pen. Open an end 10ft section a little and run them into the next pen.

Catching has to be done in daylight hours, because at dusk or at night the birds just sit on the ground and will not move. They can be caught up in the evening before dark and held overnight in crates on the ground, then loaded very early in the morning to arrive with the customer at 6 or 7am the same morning.

The author catching up young French partridges

Counting and crating the birds.

A nice pen of birds in the Catcher.

Each crate has a corrugated cardboard sheet cut to size, covering the floor. Some people use straw, but the sheet is quicker and easier to clean out. The crates are stacked onto a trailer, with a metal framework over the floor to raise them up about 4 inches. This is important because rainwater can collect on the floor of the trailer, and when it is on the move, a surge of water can soak the birds in the bottom crates. The trailer must have a special tarpaulin with straps to cover the end release gates on the crates, just in case they become jolted open during the journey. On showery days, sideboards are put at the back and front of the trailer to protect the birds from spray thrown up by the vehicle in front, and passing vehicles.

If long journeys are undertaken it is best to travel through the latter part of the night and early morning. This way it is cooler for the birds and there is less traffic about, meaning a faster journey time. The birds are then released at first light ready for feeding.

Note the raised crates for better ventilation, and to prevent the birds in the bottom crates getting soaked on wet days.

The Release Pen.

The number of release pens and locations will depend on the number of birds put down.

You need to place the pens strategically to ensure they get maximum sunshine, are not too exposed to the prevailing wind and are planted with a cover crop which is well grown at the point when the birds are released, normally the end of July, August, and September.

The cover crop is normally kale or maize with mixtures of sunflower, rape, quinoa and cereals, which not only provide cover from winged vermin but also natural food, which is excellent for wild birds as well. There should be open rides cut through this crop where the birds can get dry, sunbathe, and dust if the weather permits.

Some release pens may hold 200 birds, some about 1000, so size is important as you will need to hold the birds up for several weeks, before letting them out in dribs and drabs. This way the release pen becomes home or a base which they come back to if they are disturbed or wish to feed. In the old days, broodies which had hatched and reared the chicks, were also put out in the release pens complete with their coops, and this helped to draw the young birds back if they strayed too far.

A release pen showing the electric fences against foxes and badgers.

The release pens are constructed in a different way from the rearing pens but are made of the same materials. The number of birds to be released will dictate the size of the pens; these are normally 20 or 30ft wide i.e. 2 or 3 x 10ft sections, with a gate for access each end, and can be anything from 40 to 120ft long. You will need to cut a 6ft wide track in the cover crop all the way round to make room for this construction to be put up, and to allow the fox proof fence to work properly

The sections are supported by 6ft to 8ft wooden posts and held together with plastic ties. Along the sunny side, instead of sections there is a long green plastic curtain hung on plain wire; at the bottom it is turned outwards and laid along the ground, and large stones are placed along it to hold it down. This is eventually raised and removed so the birds have free access all the time.

A 1.5" Netlon canopy is slung over the whole pen and supported by 10ft posts which stand along the middle of the pen: these are fitted with large disks of plyboard nailed to the top to prevent the netting from chafing and breaking. Inside, the 10ft sections are draped with green netting which is suspended from the canopy to waist height to make partitions within the pen. The purpose of this green netting is to prevent the partridges from flying too far and too fast, getting up speed and killing themselves or bursting through the wire.

The birds feed from waterproof hoppers, and bell drinkers or nipple drinkers are provided with a header tank. At this stage the minimum of disturbance is essential, with the supply of food and water managed every two or three days. It goes without saying that the birds are very vulnerable now, and vermin control night and day is called for, as a loss of ten birds represents about £250-00.

The release pen is a temporary construction and is only in use for 6 to 8 weeks.

A nipple drinking system and header tank. The water pipe with the drinking nipples attached is raised on wooden stakes about 9 inches - 23cm off the ground.

The release crates are open and the birds are ready to walk or fly out. The blue container is a food hopper. Note the well grown kale cover.

Releasing the birds.

The birds are brought in by trailer, normally 35 birds per crate. They are unloaded in the crates through the access door and placed on the ground. The end exit door is opened. Some birds walk out, some fly out and one or two just sit in the crate. These are shooed out by opening the top sliding door. Once empty, the crates are removed and put back on the trailer. The pen is left quiet for the rest of the day. The drinkers and hoppers will have to be checked in the late afternoon, to make sure that they are working. It is worthwhile just whistling while you do this so the birds recognise you and are a little more relaxed in your presence.

The birds arrive in their covered trailer. Note the straps covering the exit doors to prevent accidental opening during the journey.

Birds bunching up just prior to release.

The crates are passed through a door into the release pen.

Some birds fly out like bullets but the netlon baffles prevent any damage to them.

Young adult French partridges on a release crate.

Tagging.

Partridges are not all tagged these days and do not wear leg rings or bands. It has been found that leg rings become brittle with age and are a serious hazard to French partridges which run about far more than the English, and the rings can get caught in couch grass or baler twine.

The tagging process is done with a special hand held applicator, which inserts the plastic tag in the flap of skin in the wing by the body. This area of skin has relatively few blood vessels and therefore there is little or no blood. The tags are quite small so that they don't impede the bird's flight; they come in various colours and can be numbered as well, but can only be read when the bird is being handled. They are fitted after the birds have been caught, prior to release.

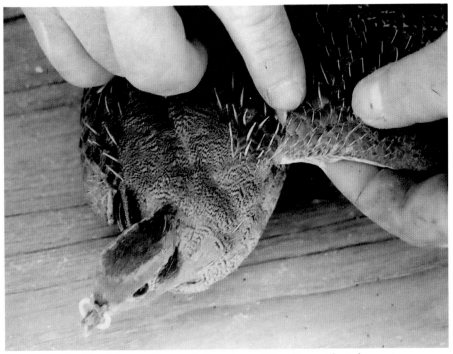

An English partridge ready for release. The bit must be taken out, and the index finger shows where the tag is to be inserted.

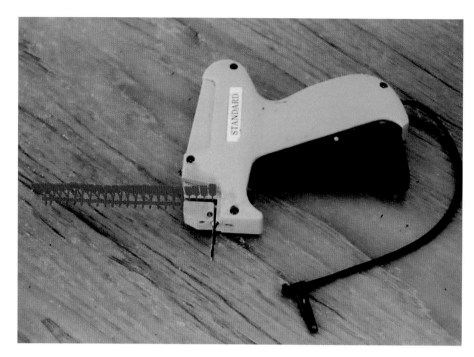

The plastic tag gun.

The tag being inserted into the skin behind the wing bone.

54

Laying Pens and Feeding.

Let us look at the history of laying pens.

There was and is a large demand for partridge eggs; in order to supply that demand, the Game Conservancy and several estates tried and trialled various methods of penning birds for breeding. This was considered preferable to importing all the eggs from France where the breeding pens are smaller and not as sophisticated as those developed in the UK. Defra have just awarded a contract for research into raised laying units and a three year investigation is to take place with the report to be produced in 2012.

It's important to realise that partridges are monogamous, i.e. they breed in pairs unlike pheasants which are flock mated. Partridges used to be over wintered in flocks in large pens, but this system was abandoned because of high loses due to fighting and disease. Next, pairs of partridge were put in pens roughly 2.5 x 2.5 metres, (8 x 8 ft) on grass, but this created another set of problems. First, these pens had to be moved regularly in order to keep the birds on fresh ground. This proved to be expensive: moving 500 or more pens, feeding, watering, and egg collecting on a regular basis was very time consuming. Then there was the disturbance caused to the birds while looking for eggs in the pens, plus problems with ground borne disease. To add to this, once the hen English partridge had made a scrape (nest) she was always determined to lay in the same place which made moving pens a nightmare, and on flinty ground she had a habit of rolling egg-sized flints into the nest which broke the real ones. There was also a problem with French partridges which were constantly on the move, so their feet would become balled up with mud meaning that they couldn't mate properly so this method was abandoned.

So some radical thinking was necessary. Finally, the system was developed which is used today: in October pairs of partridge are put into 8ft runs raised about 3ft off the ground, which cuts out all the difficulties with disease, fighting and mud balled feet. There is roughly a 5% problem of pairs not getting on, so you will need a few extra cock birds and hens available to change partners around if necessary.

The pens are made in blocks of five; each pen is 8ft long (the 8ft sides being made of solid plyboard), 12ins high and 14ins wide; the floors are wire mesh. Either end of the run is a covered shelter; one has a food hopper and

A laying or breeding pen set up.

Note the water line supplying the nipple drinkers with a header tank at the end.

top swinging door which protects the food from the weather and prevents birds from flying out of the pen when the hopper is being filled up. It also allows access with a small padded net to catch any bird for inspection. The other covered shelter has a solid floor and is in two sections with a nest box in one. The floor has a layer of coarse sand where the birds can dust bath, lay and pick up grit.

These pens greatly reduce the labour costs of feeding and egg collection while ensuring the birds are dry under foot and have plenty of natural sun light and room to run up and down. Also, they are unable to see their neighbours, which prevents fighting. They have two shelters, a food hopper and fresh water via a nipple drinking system. There is no bitting involved and saddles are unnecessary.

Although the birds are on wire mesh floors, their feet do not suffer, and their droppings fall through to the ground below. The roof of the pen is 1.5" Netlon, so if the birds are frightened and try to fly up, they don't scalp themselves, but just bounce off.

The pens are placed in a quiet, gently sloping area which is open to the sunshine but not windy. Partridges love sun bathing. Most birds settle down well in these pens, but are nervous of any visitors to the area.

A line of breeding pens. Note the wind baffle on the right.

A French male partridge. The female is inspecting the laying area.

A pair of English partridges.

How long are the birds penned up? Most people hold their pairs for about 10 months from October to July, until after they have laid, others for two breeding seasons, and the French for three seasons. The first year the hen bird will lay about 40-50 eggs, the next year about 60-70 eggs and the third year 50-60. They are then moved with the early young birds into release pens. English partridges tend to attach themselves to other coveys, and the French birds, which can be more solitary, remain in pairs.

Water

As already mentioned water is via nipple drinkers. A 1 inch pipe is attached to a 6 to 8 gallon header tank which is fed from the mains water supply via a stopcock and ball valve. The pipe is laid along the top of the pens and attached to each drinker. Vitamins, medicines, and cider vinegar can be administrated to the birds via the header tank and pipe line. If there is a leaking drinker, the water drips down through the wire mesh, and therefore doesn't create a health problem. This form of drinker is the best as there is no cleaning involved and no build up of disease.

Feeding

One of the most important aspects of keeping partridges is feeding them properly: only the best will do (dusty food should be avoided at all costs), and it is necessary to build up a good rapport with your supplier. For the smaller operation, food can be supplied in bags, for larger concerns the food arrives by lorry and is blown into a hopper near the rearing field. A small trailer pulled by a quad bike is then backed up under the hopper to collect the food which is distributed in the houses from a plastic bucket or jug. Quad bikes are popular and convenient as they are quick, light and fairly quiet, and leave little impression on the grass.

Every 3 or 4 days the birds are fed special partridge pellets which come in varying percentages of protein: there are maintenance (14%), pre-breeder (17.5) and breeder pellets (20%). They are fed in hoppers or troughs with a plastic guard to minimise wastage. These hoppers and troughs require regular cleaning as they always collect a build up of food dust.

Two types of food hopper used in breeding pens.

Note the plastic netting in front of the feed trough to prevent the birds from getting in.

Egg collection

The laying period is from early March through to June, with the birds in full lay by the middle of March. The first few eggs of the season are not very fertile particularly from young birds, and the last ones of the season can also be unreliable. They are usually laid on the sand in the nest boxes although some are to be found on the weld mesh floor. Eggs are collected in the late morning or early afternoon as the birds tend to lay between 10 and 12 in the morning. They are normally collected in plastic coated wire baskets ready for washing. As the egg collector does the daily rounds, so he or she flags up any problems there might be: everyone has a different system, be it the use of clothes pegs or coloured plastic cards. The eggs are transferred to the pre-setting room.

Lighting

The further north you are situated, the more beneficial it will be to install a lighting system above the pens; in the southern counties of England this is barely necessary. A waterproof line of light bulbs is arranged above the pens with a timing system. In January the lights are switched on in the morning only, and stepped up gradually week by week to give a 14 hour day by early March.

Setting up the site

As we have already mentioned, finding the right site is all important.

It should be gently sloping for the gravity fed drinking water, sheltered from the winds yet sunny, away from the public gaze and footpaths and with good vehicle access for bringing food in and eggs out, etc. There should a lockable metal cabin for food storage, records, medicines, and somewhere to shelter. The whole site must be surrounded by a fox proof fence and electric wire, to prevent the birds being harried in the pens. Signs of fox invasion are holes in the top Netlon wire and the birds gone or maimed, or a bird with its legs nipped off when a fox tried to pull it through the wire mesh floor. Most people cover the site with nylon netting to prevent problems with hawks, corvids, owls and buzzards, and also in case a bird escapes from a pen.

Cleaning

This is done in August, as a line of pens becomes free when the birds have been released. The water pipe is removed along with the food hoppers and top Netlon, and the group of five pens is all moved sideways. This allows room for muck clearance by a machine such as a Bobcat. The pens can then be removed to another site for cleaning, repair and wood preserving. It is important to plan for this space when setting up the laying pens.

Repenishing the food hoopers.

French partridge eggs in a collecting basket.

Preparation of Eggs

The eggs are collected in plastic coated wire baskets and brought in to be washed. Some people do not wash their eggs but clean any that need it with sand paper. Because they have come from the laying pens they are generally very clean, but it is as well to sanitise them before they are set; this is optional. There are several egg disinfectants on the market such as Deosan or Antec, as well as various egg washers, the Rotamaid being one of the most popular. The water needs to be heated to approximately 80 degrees F and the disinfectant added as per the manufacturer's instructions. The wire basket of eggs is lowered into the water which swishes round in a timed rotating movement. When it has finished the basket is lifted out and the eggs are allowed to dry. They are then inspected for any cracks or dents before being placed in the incubator trays. They vary in shade quite a lot, with the same birds normally laying the same colour.

English partridge eggs.

French partridge eggs - twice the size of English partridge eggs

Bought in eggs

Most eggs come over from France by lorry. They will be clean and can be loaded into incubator trays before being fumigated. They should then be rested for 24 to 48 hours before being put into the incubators; the temperature in the resting room should be between 12 and 15 degrees C. It is good practice to pre-warm the eggs before they are put into the incubators to avoid a major temperature shock; bring the temperature up from around 15 to 24 degrees C for about 12 hours before setting them. (Embryonic development usually starts at about 25 degrees C.)

Your own eggs

These do not need to be fumigated. Once they have been washed (optional) and inspected, they are placed in incubator trays which are rocked from side to side during incubation. Large walk-in incubators have special wheeled 'dollies'; the trays of eggs are loaded onto these and all turned together, regularly throughout the incubation period. When not in use the dollies can be wheeled into the rest room for storage.

Checking and loading the eggs into the incubator trays.

64

Incubation

Today most of the problems associated with incubation have been ironed out by electronics, but the machines must be serviced regularly in order to run smoothly; if an incubator is one tenth of a degree out it will mean that the eggs hatch too early or too late. Micro-management can be vital to help with the timing of a hatch so that you can organise your work force to be available when needed.

You must set your incubator at 99.7degrees F for partridge eggs with 55% humidity. On the nineteenth day the eggs are moved to the hatcher which is set at 98.7 degrees F with humidity at about 100%. The total incubation and hatching period is 23 days.

Before the eggs are moved into the hatcher they are taken out of the incubation trays and put into hatching trays which are lined with paper to give the chicks a firm foothold (to prevent splayed legs) and stop debris dropping from one to another. These trays are then put into the hatcher which is in a separate room away from the incubator(s). Hatching is the dirty part of the incubation process, with dust, fluff and bits of egg shell getting everywhere. The eggs take 6 hours to hatch.

Part of the author's incubation and hatching machinery.

Out of the hatcher

The hatching trays are removed from the hatcher and the chicks taken out and put into chick boxes. They will be quite lively by now with the odd one escaping to the floor.

A nice tray of newly hatched French partridge chicks.

It's essential to wear a mask and apron for this job, and women do better as they are far quicker and more nimble fingered than men. The chick boxes sometimes have 1, 2 or 4 compartments but normally have 4, with 3 compartments of 38 and 1 of 39 chicks, totalling 153 which includes the 2% surplus, the industry norm.

The chicks are moved from the hatching trays to a holding area where they are counted and put into travelling boxes.

There is silence in the packing room as everybody counts. The 2 compartments on one side are filled first then covered by half the lid which sits upside down on top; the box is swivelled round, the other side is filled and the lid pushed over to cover the whole box. The top is then given a knock which causes the chicks inside to cower down; this gives the operator time to flip it over and secure it safely without trapping any heads inside.

Chicks being counted into a four compartment travelling box.

A hatch will normally be 75 to 80% successful but is likely to be lower at the beginning and end of the egg laying season.

At this point the chicks either go to your own rearing fields or are delivered to your customers. Transport must be carefully organised as you will need a temperature controlled van, and to prevent problems of dust inhalation you should use shredded paper as litter in the chick boxes.

Empty, dead in shell or infertile eggs.

At the end all that is left in the trays are egg shells, full eggs that haven't hatched and the odd chick that hasn't made it. This debris is put through a macerator that pulverises everything into a thick soup which is sent away for incineration. The paper lining the hatching trays is burned, and the trays are washed and sterilised ready to be used again next time.

The macerator

When the Birds Have Gone

When the birds have left the rearing field the job of dismantling the pens, houses and shelters begins. (The gas bottles were removed earlier when the birds reached 8 weeks old and no longer required heat.) By catching time the houses are empty except for dirty litter.

Now that the birds have gone the drinkers and feeders can be removed. The houses and shelters are dismantled and the various components are stacked onto wooden pallets, with anything that needs mending put to one side. The roof netting is then taken off, rolled up and tied every three feet. It's important to label this with information on how many pens it will cover so you will know next year: an anonymous roll in a bag looks like any other roll.

Shelters and sections on pallets.

Stakes for the sections on pallets.

Now the sections can come down along with the stakes and plastic ties. Remember, there are three different types of section: plain 10ft ones, 10ft sections with a door and 10ft sections with a pop hole. Again, check them over and put aside any that need to be repaired.

This equipment is next taken back to the farm and power washed with disinfectant. It is then put back onto the pallets, tied down and left to dry under cover. The house sections and the two wooden floors, one from the house and one from the shelter, are also power washed, allowed to dry, and creosoted. They are then left under cover to dry again.

Now everything is ready for the next season.

Roof netting is coiled up, labelled and bagged.

Housing sections are creosoted.

Conservation of the English Partridge.

Taking steps to conserve English partridges on your land will also greatly benefit other birds as well, providing them with vital habitat and food, and maintaining the right conditions for wild flowers, butterflies and insects.
As stated before, breeding partridges are the barometer of your farmland. If you do not have partridges breeding on your land, you will probably not have a wealth of other birds, and with no partridges your farm can sometimes look and sound rather empty.

An excellent cover crop and sunning area for partridges.

So here are a few tips to make your land partridge friendly. Of course a lot will depend on the soil, as English partridges prefer lighter arable soil to clay. French partridges are not so fussy but they tend to like dryer conditions.
Because English partridges enjoy a wide range of food like insects, seeds, plant food and grain, (in fact a far more diverse diet than that of the Frenchmen) it is important that a range of food is available to them all the year round. This is where brood cover crops sown in strips with grain feeders are invaluable, particularly on wheat growing farms. The problem is that English partridges love all the weeds as well for aphids etc, so it is important to have some weedy areas on a non-organic farm. Remember, partridges are not the only ones to benefit from these strips. Stubble fields left after harvest also play a good part in holding the birds although they are unfashionable now.

In the South West of England, there is a 1000 acre farm run by two brothers who are committed to keeping and increasing English partridges on their land. They do not employ a gamekeeper. The farm is intensively run, with a production rotation of winter wheat, rape, linseed, and beans. There are several 5 acre grass meadows dotted round the farm for making hay, and about 120 acres under HLS grant aided schemes. Some hedges have a 6 metre grass strip either side, and each alternate one has a 10 metre brood cover crop as well. This consists of a mixture of grain or seed bearing plants like quinoa, teasel, millet, sunflower, and cover crops like rape and kale. All this has led to an increase in partridges, lapwings, skylarks, yellowhammers and hares; it has also resulted in a dramatic increase in butterflies and wild flowers like cowslips and violets.

Crop   2m margin   nesting area   food hopper   cover crop   crop

Leave as much space as possible for the grass bank under the fence. The south side is where the partridges will nest.

In areas where there are no hedges, a semi-permanent strip between two crops can be devoted to partridges and other birds like skylarks and lapwings. Here two grant aided beetle banks are made. Beetles help to control aphids on crops.

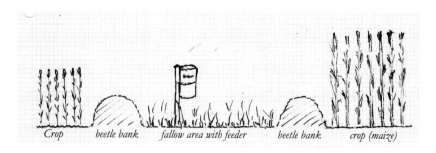

Crop   beetle bank   fallow area with feeder   beetle bank   crop (maize)

Farmers have to work closely with Defra and other conservation agencies to obtain the maximum of grant aid to offset the loss in crop production. None of this work would be of any use however, if there were not a rigid predator control programme in operation as well.

Hedges and banks play an important part in the conservation of partridges and many other birds, insects and plants, so it's important that they are properly maintained. Normally there is a trimming or cutting cycle of 2 or 3 years, but some hedgerow plants like ash, willow and elm which are fast growing, need trimming every 2 years for the hedge to remain viable and stock proof. Blackthorn, which is good for Brown Hairstreak butterflies, has a habit of creeping into the field, so it needs to be mown or cut back yearly. The size and shape of a hedge is important: it should be no higher than 2 to 3 metres with sloping sides meaning that the hedge is wider at the bottom.

3 passes with a hedge trimmer.   *A contractor's hedge.*

Hedges that are cut square are more convenient for the hedge trimmer but useless for wild birds: magpies and crows can easily perch on the top, look in and spot any nests; and when rain is blown against a hedge like this, it produces a waterfall effect down the flat side which could possibly soak a partridge trying to sit, or worse, flood the scrape and eggs.

Partridge nests are often found on the south side of a hedge, to get the best of the early morning sun and shelter from the prevailing winds. The nest is a shallow scrape with an entrance tunnel through the long grass. There is an exit via the middle of the hedge. The nest will often be sheltered by a thorny branch or bramble.

Sometimes a hedge is cut on one side only or the top is taken out. In order for a hedge to work well it is sometimes necessary to cut it down to 18 to 24 inches and let it regrow.

One thing is clear: if large quantities of reared English or French partridges are put down, their viability is very poor, and only small quantities of birds, 10 to 15 in well spaced groups, are feasible in August or September. If there is a barren pair of English partridges, they will sometime foster a group of young birds, and so the natural cycle will begin.

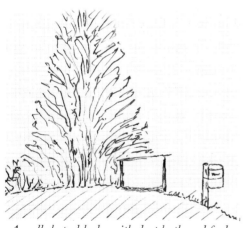

A well shaped hedge with dust bath and feeder.

A good partridge hedge.

The hedge needs to be trimmed every 2 to 3 years, alternating each side to allow one side or the other to produce natural fruit for other wildlife. Note the sloping sides to give a thick bottom to the hedge.

You will need a gap to prevent weeds from invading the crop. This area provides a good corridor for birds to move along, to take off, to dry out and to dust bath in.

Putting a dust shelter with plenty of fine ash and sand into the hedge is another way of encouraging partridges. It is just a sheet of corrugated iron on four short posts, and is out of the way of farm machinery.

Predators

Prior to setting up the rearing pens, the farms around should be swept for foxes. This means lamping at night, on several different occasions. You don't want a litter of cubs near the rearing field.

Most of the time, and certainly during the early part of the rearing season, there is so much activity going on that there is little problem from foxes; but it is towards the end of the rearing season, when fox cubs are starting to move around because of disturbance at harvest time, that problems can occur. That is why it is important to have an electric fence surrounding the rearing pens and working day and night.

A fox proof fence. The grass has been killed under the electric wires.

As the birds are enclosed there is little problem from winged vermin, except for escapees, those birds that have found a hole in the wire netting of a section or in the Netlon on top; most of them are never seen again. These birds are at risk mainly from sparrow hawks and buzzards (and foxes). The holes must be found and repaired, as potentially you are losing £6-00 every time a bird gets out. Most partridge breeders have catching pens; these are moveable pens with one way entrances which are placed outside the rearing pens with food and water inside to entice the birds in. A landing net works well too. This shows the importance of keeping the grass round the pens nice and short, so you can see any birds that have got out.

Different catching pens for escapees.

Proper predator control is also vital in the release areas. Although the release pens should be surrounded by electric fencing, when the pen is fully opened up a fox can cause damage, so prior to the birds being released a programme of fox control is required.

At this stage, buzzards, which are fully protected, can be a nuisance, particularly just as it gets dark, so be aware of this.

It is quite interesting to note that when a hawk, buzzard, kite or microlight plane passes above, the partridges go quiet and crouch on the ground with one eye on the aerial threat.

It is a good idea to have a series of tunnel traps in place by the gateways to pick up any ground vermin. These will catch the odd stoat or weasel and maybe a mink or two but the main catch will be rats. It is worth spending a little time on these, building them into the hedge or bank so they look inconspicuous to the passerby, but you can check them from the car.

For further reading please see Modern Vermin Control in the Gold Cockerel Series.

The work of a hen sparrowhawk.

Partridge Diseases

Any concentrations of stock will always increase the risk of disease, whether brought in by wild birds, animals or the wind. It is vital to be able to detect by sight or smell, the first signs of potential problems and take precautions before they become really serious.

Both English and French partridges originated in warmer and drier Southern climates, and therefore drink very little. It is important to be aware of this as some drugs are water borne, and if the weather is wet the birds often prefer to take droplets of water from the wire netting rather than their drinkers. Once the poults are 8 or 10 weeks old, they will be very fussy drinkers, so blackcurrent juice is mixed with the water to mask the taste of the drugs.

Rearing partridges can be relatively straightforward in dry years, but during a wet year like 2008, all sorts of problems occur, and the partridge rearer has to be very vigilant indeed and work closely with his avian vet to avoid disease in the birds.

It is important to realise that some of the diseases that affect partridges show few if any symptoms early on, and it is not until later, when the bird is really sick and has probably infected many others, or has died, that you realise something is wrong. This is why it is so important to have weekly post mortems of at least 2 birds from each batch, so you can give your stock the right medication when necessary before things get out of hand. Biosecurity is the first step in preventing disease, and it's always advisable to dip boots before entering any pen.

So let us look at the diseases which can affect partridges.

Protozoa Infections

Histomoniasis (Blackhead)
Symptoms: young birds die suddenly, older birds are lethargic and lose weight, some birds are scouring (yellow).
Prevention: worming routinely and avoiding infected ground.
Cause: this is caused by protozoa which multiply very rapidly in the gut before being expelled in the droppings. They survive in Heterakis eggs in the environment, and are sometimes also carried by earthworms. It can be caused by spreading poultry manure on fields.
Treatment: Tiamutin, Tetracycline.
Mortality: medium to high.

Hexamitiasis
Symptoms: birds look off colour and lethargic; they stop flying and often have frothy yellow droppings, leading to death.
Cause: small protozoa which are capable of moving independently and spontaneously, and are found in the small intestine. They are common in the summer months.
Prevention: rotation of rearing grounds. Try to keep the pens dry.
Treatment: Tiamutin, Tetracyclines.
Mortality: medium to high.

Trichomoniasis
Symptoms: these are very similar to those of Hexamitiasis with birds off colour and lethargic etc.
Cause: small mobile protozoa which are very difficult to detect unless the birds are post mortemed and examined thoroughly.
Prevention: this disease is caused by stress from poor management, overcrowding, hunger, thirst or being moved incorrectly etc; good management is always of paramount importance to avoid disease in your partridges. Trichomoniasis is not carried in old rearing grounds.
Treatment: difficult, Tiamutin.
Mortality: medium to high.

Coccidiosis

Symptoms: birds appear lazy, with ruffled feathers and no interest in life or food. They lose weight, dehydrate and die. They can be affected at any age but are usually between 8 to 12 weeks old.

Cause: this is a protozoan parasite, the two main types being Eimeria colchici and Eimeria legionensis. The Eimeria eggs or oocysts are passed out in the droppings; an infected bird can produce millions of eggs. These are picked up by other birds, and take up residence in the small intestine, duodenum and caecal tracts, as they need warm damp conditions to develop in. Stress plays a part in this condition as well.

Prevention: as you are rearing on grass there is not much you can do except make sure that the rearing field is not used again, keep all food hoppers and drinkers regularly disinfected and use in-feed Avatec.

Treatment: Amprolium, Toltrazuril.

Mortality: low to high.

Bacteria

E-coli

Symptoms: this occurs mainly in chicks up to 5 or 6 weeks old, and is usually secondary to other diseases. The chicks stand hunched up with drooping wings, and are not interested in food or water. There is often a sweet/sour smell.

Cause: poor management or hygiene, stale food, stress, or other diseases creeping in such as mycoplasma or coccidiosis.

Prevention: a clean environment, drinkers especially.

Treatment: antibiotics that are sensitive to the bacteria.

Mortality: medium to high.

Mycoplasmosis or Mycoplasma gallisepticum

Symptoms: the birds are lethargic and sometimes lame, with discharges from eyes and nostrils. They breathe through half open beaks and in bad cases the orbital cavity (eye socket) is swollen and the nasal cavity smells putrid. In adult birds, egg production drops. It is sometimes seen in wild partridges.

Cause: it is a disease that can be spread via the egg; it is normally spread by other diseased birds via drinkers and feeders or the birds jugging together at night. It can lie dormant until stress brings it on. Some wild birds carry the disease.

Prevention: vaccination of layers will prevent egg transmission; good biosecurity.

Treatment: Tiamutin can prevent signs but birds will still be carriers.

Mortality: medium but higher with combined infections such as TRT.

Staphylococcus

Symptoms: birds become lame, often with swollen hock joints and legs at unusual angles. A few birds may die.

Cause: birds sometimes show signs of this when they have been moved from pen to pen or to the release pen, or when hard bits have been pulled out, as the bacteria may enter the bloodstream via damaged nostrils.

Prevention: avoid rough handling of birds and use soft bits or remove hard bits by clipping instead of pulling.

Treatment: Lame and emaciated birds should be culled, and an antibacterial drug administered through the water.

Mortality: Low

Viruses

Avian Influenza (a notifiable disease)

Symptoms: these can range from mild depression and decreased egg production in the laying pens to sudden high mortality rates.

Cause: a virus which causes respiratory disease. There are many strains, some more virulent than others.

Treatment: there is none as all the birds have to be slaughtered.

Infectious Bronchitis (IB) (Coronavirus) (Rarely seen in partridges.)

Symptoms: this is mainly seen in breeding stock and the egg production will be reduced. Birds are often found dead although their body condition will still be good. Sometimes there is a whitish discharge from the vent.

Cause: there are many strains of this viral disease which is spread from bird to bird by breathing, and also on equipment and the stockman's clothing. The virus attacks the kidneys and allied tubes.

Prevention: vaccination of laying stock will reduce incidence.
Treatment: none available. Reduce stress and provide electrolytes (Solulyte).
Mortality: medium to high.

Rotavirus

Symptoms: this affects chicks between 4 to 10 days old. The virus is ingested when the chicks are just starting to feed. They look cold and huddle together, and pick over their food but don't eat; they often have runny, watery droppings.

Cause: the exact cause is still unclear but it is thought that the micro-organism can be dormant in adult laying partridges, and is passed out on the shell of the egg. The organism survives on the egg in the incubator, and the chick picks up the virus when it hatches, hence the early death of very young birds.

Prevention: as this can be a rather virulent disease, you should take great care to sanitize all hatching eggs and incubation and hatching equipment. It can spread easily on clothing and boots etc.

Treatment: electrolytes (Solulyte) and antibiotics may help. Birds that survive will usually be stunted.

Mortality: can be very high.

TRT (Turkey rhinotracheitis)

Symptoms: a respiratory disease with eye and nasal discharges and a sudden drop in egg production in the laying pen.

Cause: a pneumovirus which is spread rapidly in the air.

Prevention: the best prevention is to avoid any contact with commercial chicken or turkey farms, and avoid siting your rearing grounds near or down-wind of these establishments. Feed lorries could be a source of infection as well.

Treatment: antibiotics for secondary bacterial infections.

Mortality: low unless complicated by bacteria.

Fungi

Aspergillosis
Symptoms: this occurs mainly in very young birds which have difficulty in breathing and can die within 24 hours.

Cause: inhalation of fungal spores resulting from wet or mouldy straw caused by leaking roof or drinkers.

Prevention: use paper, shavings or cardboard chips, but NOT straw. Check the drinkers regularly for blockages and overflows.

Treatment: none.

Mortality: low to medium.

Parasites

Gapes
Symptoms: the birds gasp for air with their beaks open. They lose condition and become very lethargic.

Cause: the roundworm Syngamus trachea which in its adult stage lives in the bird's windpipe, restricting its breathing and can eventually kill it. The worm is 2 to 3cms long and produces eggs in the windpipe which are coughed up by the bird and ingested before being passed out in the droppings. After a period of development the larvae/eggs attach themselves to insects or earthworms and can live like this for several years. A partridge then eats the insect or earthworm and the larvae/eggs hatch in the gut and make their way to the lungs where they develop into worms, then move to the windpipe and start the cycle again.

Prevention: a good rotation of rearing fields and a strategic worming programme.

Treatment: an infeed treatment of Flubenvet before the birds are let out of the shelter pen.

Mortality: can be very heavy in young reared birds.

Intestinal Worms: Capillaria (hairworm) and Ascaridia (roundworm)

Symptoms: none at first except that the birds are not doing as well as they should. They start to lose weight, sometimes there is diarrhoea with blood, then they begin to die.

Cause: the hairworms bore through the wall of the gut causing digestion problems which lead to weakness, diarrhoea and death. Roundworms cause ill thrift.

Prevention: rotation of rearing grounds is essential.

Treatment: worming with Flubenvet.

Mortality: low to high for Capillaria.

Lice

Symptoms: slight loss of feathers under the beak and on the upper neck in laying birds often 2 years old or more.

Cause: lice (mallophaga) often brought in by wild birds, overcrowding.

Prevention: biosecurity.

Treatment: Ivermectin in the water.

Mortality: low.

Scaley Legs

Symptoms: raised scales on the feet and lower legs, lameness and swollen legs, seen only in breeding pens of adults.

Cause: this is caused by a mite Cnemidocoptes mutans which is brought in by wild birds, and overcrowding.

Prevention: biosecurity.

Treatment: Ivermectin in the water.

Mortality: low.

Physical Problems
(mainly due to poor management)

Chilling and Smothering
Signs: chicks or young birds huddled together to keep warm, birds being trampled and smothered.
Cause: there are many possible causes – the heat source, gas heater/electric hen not working or too hot, gas turned too low, panic caused by sudden noise, an owl call or hailstorm for instance, causing crowding.
Treatment: there is none.
Mortality: low to medium.

Feather pecking, tail, toe, wing and shoulder
Signs: blood on the tail, toe, wing or shoulder, a few dead birds, and in extreme cases cannibalism.
Cause: can be single or several – the house too hot, gas set too high on hot thundery days, poor quality food, no water, too much light in the house, overcrowding, poor ventilation, fighting, stress due to disturbance.
Treatment: be aware of these potential problems. Bitting is the normal way to stop feather pecking, but try to find the underlying cause.

Starve outs
Symptoms: day old chicks looking listless with pale withered legs.
Cause: poor quality hatching eggs, poor conditions in the brooder house, and long journey times.
Prevention: improve conditions in the brooder house – get rid of draughts, check litter, temperature, freshness of food, cut down delivery journey time if possible.
Treatment: use of an electrolyte additive (Solulyte) in the water can encourage the chicks to eat, drink and hydrate.
Mortality: there should be no more than 2 to 3% per batch.

Sun exposure

Signs: birds gasping for air with a few dead ones.

Cause: mainly seen on very hot days in young adult birds from 8 to 14 weeks old, if there is no shade in the pen.

Prevention: all pens should have a roll or two of 5m shading netting available, which can be pulled across the top of the pens to provide shade when necessary.

Mortality: low.

Mud balled feet. These birds are unsaleable.

Mud balled feet

Signs: mud balls caked onto the end of toes, feet and legs. This is particularly seen in French partridges, and can be a sign of diarrhoea.

Cause: muddy pens. The sun comes out and dries the pens but leaves the birds with hard baked balls of mud on their feet.

Prevention: put down straw round the edges of the pen where the birds run up and down. Straw is also useful because it soaks up the water thus stopping the birds from drinking it, important if you are medicating their water, but there could be a risk of Aspergillosis if you use straw.

Treatment: the mud balls can be very gently cut off or picked off with a pen knife.

Health Tips

Healthy birds should spend their time running up and down and flying round their pens; if they are just sitting on the ground and not flying, there is a problem.

It is vital to clean drinkers and feeders twice a week to ensure there is no build up of bacteria and algae.

Always feed your youngest stock first and your medicated stock last.

Good bio-security is essential around the pens.

USEFUL CONTACTS

Antec International	www.ahs.dupont.com
Ashley Game Services	tel: 01769 520226
Attleborough Accessories	www.attacc.com
Autonest Ltd	tel: 01536 760332
Brinsea Incubators	www.brinsea.co.uk
Collins Nets	tel: 01308 427352
Gamekeepa Feeds Ltd	www.gamekeepafeeds.co.uk
Hatch-It Incubators	www.hatchitincubators.com
Knowle Nets	www.knowlenets.co.uk
Parkland Auto Feeders	www.parklandproducts.co.uk
Patrick Pinker	www.patrickpinker.com
Natureform Europe Ltd	www.natureform.biz
Southern Partridges Ltd	tel: 01769 560505
St. David's Game Bird Services	tel: 01392 872932
The Game Conservancy Trust	www.gameconservancy.org.uk
The Game Farmer's Association	www.gfa.org.uk

Index

Aspergillosis 26, 32, 85, 88
Avian Influenza 83
Avian vet 11, 80
Badgers 47
Bitting 36, 57, 87
Blackhead 81
Breeding 1, 5, 6, 10, 55, 56, 57, 59, 60, 73, 83, 86
Brooder House 87
Caecal tracts 82
Cannibalism 36, 87
Catching 13, 14, 41, 42, 43, 44, 71, 78
Chilling 87
Coccidiosis 82
Conservation 73, 75
Costs 13, 57, 59
Cover crop 47, 48, 73, 74
Crates 10, 42, 44, 46, 49, 50, 51
Crows 75
Diseases 11, 80, 82
Drinkers 13, 22, 25, 29, 30, 31, 33, 34, 35, 39, 48, 50, 56, 59, 71, 80, 82, 83, 85, 89
Dust bath 76
E-Coli 82
Egg collection 57
Egg trays 10
Electric fencing 79
Electrolytes 84
Feeders 39, 71, 73, 83, 89, 90, 91
Feeding 5, 27,35, 46, 55, 57, 59,
Fencing 79
Flubenvet 85, 86
Food 35 36, 59
Foxes 47, 77, 78
Gapes 85, 91
Gas heater 27
Hatcher 65, 66
Hatching eggs 10, 84, 87

Header tank 26, 48, 49, 56, 59
Hexamitiasis 81
Humidity 65
Incubation 3, 5, 64, 65, 84
Infectious Bronchitis (IB) 83
Laying pens 10, 55, 62, 63, 83
Leg rings 53
Lice 86
Lighting 27, 29 61
Litter 26, 27, 32, 33, 69, 71, 77, 87
Medication 80
Mud balled feet 39, 55, 88
Mycoplasma 82, 91
Netting 24, 25, 39, 48, 60, 61, 71, 72, 78, 80, 88
Plumage 6
Predators 77
Rats 79
Rearing field 22, 59, 71, 77, 82
Release pens 47, 48, 59, 79
Sexing 8, 6
Sheep 11, 12, 24
Smothering 87
Spurs 1, 5, 6
Staphylococcus 83
Starve outs 87
Sun exposure 88
Tagging 53
Traps 79
Trichomoniasis 81
TRT 83, 84
Ventilation 13, 27, 35, 46, 87
Vermin 47, 48, 78, 79
Vitamins 59
Washing eggs 64
Worms 85, 86
Washing eggs 64
Worms 85, 86